Roman Mythology
Grades 5–8

Educational Impressions
257-5AP

Creative Experiences in
ROMAN MYTHOLOGY

Written by
Vowery Carlile

Illustrated by
Karen Birchak

The purchase of this book entitles the individual teacher to reproduce copies of the student pages for use in his or her classroom exclusively. The reproduction of any part of the work for an entire school or school system or for commercial use is prohibited.

ISBN 1-56644-257-5 (10-digit)
978-1-56644-257-2 (13-digit)
© 2007 Educational Impressions, Inc., Hawthorne, NJ

EDUCATIONAL IMPRESSIONS, INC.
Hawthorne, NJ 07507

Printed in the United States of America.

Table of Contents

To the Teacher

This book is part of the Creative Expressions in Mythology Series. It contains a series of mythology stories with each having a vocabulary lesson, discussion questions, creative questions and extra activities that involve creative writing, designs or projects.

DIRECTIONS:

Step 1: Begin the unit by introducing the vocabulary words on the vocabulary activity sheet. (These words are underlined in the stories.) Ask the students to look up the definitions and write them on their sheets. Many of the vocabulary lessons include a section where the student must use the vocabulary words to write a brief paragraph about the story. This will need to be completed after reading the myth.

Step 2: Read the myth, individually or together, and use the comprehension/discussion questions to talk about the story. The vocabulary lesson sheet can be completed now if it involves a writing activity.

Step 3: The students are now ready to complete the creative questions. These questions are all asked at the upper levels of Bloom's Taxonomy. The questions are designed to encourage students to think at a higher level and not just repeat information learned in the story. Many of the questions involve no right or wrong answers; therefore, grading will be subjective. I suggest that you look for creative answers using knowledge gained from the myth.

Step 4: When the creative questions have been answered, you may let students pick out one or all of the extra activities. These activities include creative writing, illustrating, design or creating something new that will support the myth. These can be assigned or done for extra credit.

Step 5: After reading some or all the myths, students can participate in the research-project unit. Directions are given.

The objectives of this book are to encourage students to learn about mythology, to use the acquired learning and to develop something new through a research project. In today's society, research is so important for the students. The skills needed to complete research will be used through college and careers. Educators must give students the skills to successfully complete research beginning in elementary school. Through the use of this book, opportunities will be made available for students to produce a project that will bring satisfaction to them and the teacher.

Introduction

The mention of ancient Rome brings thoughts of the greatest empire on earth. According to Roman myths, the surviving twin son of Mars, Romulus, founded Rome. The empire began as a dream and eventually overtook Western Europe, North Africa and the Middle East.

The legacy of ancient Rome still survives in our world today. Roman architecture can be seen in many modern buildings. Central heat, running water, bathrooms, concrete and political structures are a few marvels left to us by the Romans.

Historians believe that Rome began around 800 BCE as a group of huts, built by the Latin people. The huts evolved into groups of wooden buildings, which in turn grew into cities. The first city was ruled by Romulus, who was followed by three kings. Not much is known about those three, but the fourth, Tarquinius Priscus, seized power around 616 BCE and began to build cities out of stone. This was the beginning of the great Roman Empire.

After the Roman people experienced a tyrant king, a group rebelled and expelled the king. They set up the Republic of Rome, which was governed by Roman patricians, the city's most important and richest male citizens. Three hundred of these men sat in the Senate. They discussed public affairs and made new laws. This worked for a while until the rich families began to argue with each other, finally causing chaos in the government. One group would take over, then another. This went on for years.

Even with the fussing in the government, Rome was a mighty nation. Its greatness was largely based on the powerful Roman army. The army was well equipped and trained to fight any nation. Most historians agree that the Roman army was the most successful fighting force in history.

According to ancient beliefs, the success of Rome was due to many gods and goddesses helping them. The Romans needed a way to explain why natural occurrences took place, so they eventually adopted Greek gods and goddesses, giving them Roman names.

Creative Experiences in Roman Mythology addresses nine of those myths. Following each myth is vocabulary practice, discussion questions, creative-thinking questions and creative writing and other activities. At the end of the book is a research-project unit.

Throughout history the Roman Empire has been studied because of its greatness. Teachers and students will enjoy reading myths from one of the greatest civilizations on earth.

The Beginning of Roman Mythology

Stories of Roman gods and goddesses were passed down by word of mouth and some stories were written about them. Most of the early mythology had to do with the founding of Rome and was based on the legend of Romulus and Remus. Although they had a <u>pantheon</u> of gods and goddesses, they did not believe that their gods took human shapes, nor did they worship them in temples. The Romans thought of their gods as powers rather than as people. They believed that objects and events had <u>supernatural</u> forces.

The Romans were not makers of myths and there is not really a pure Roman mythology. When the Romans conquered Greece, however, they adopted many of the the Greek ways, including their mythology. Many of the deities were similar in character to the Greek deities, but the Roman poets who wrote about them changed their names, giving them Roman names. At that time they also began to picture their deities in human form with human characteristics.

People began to use the actions of the deities to explain the natural occurrences they did not understand. The most important was Jupiter, king of all gods and goddesses; Juno was his wife and queen. Other important gods and goddesses included Cupid, god of love; Mars, the war god; Venus, goddess of love and beauty; Pluto, god of the underworld; Vulcan, god of fire; and Neptune, god of the sea. Still others included Vesta, goddess of the <u>hearth</u> fire; Neptunus,the god of the life-giving rain and spring weather; Terminus, the god of the boundary stone; Pomona, the goddess of fruit trees; Ventumnus, god of changing seasons; and Flora, goddess of flowers.

The Romans had many ceremonies that were used to worship their gods and goddesses. One such <u>ritual</u> involved the family, which was at the heart of the Roman religion. The family needed divine help to be successful in work and life. The head of the family was responsible for this ritual. He would have to place a small gift in the family <u>shrine</u> each day. The gift might be incense, food or wine.

Another ceremony involved the farm family. At the end of the farming year a festival called Compitalia was celebrated. Each family hung a plough, a wooden doll representing every free person living in the household, and a woolen ball for each slave in the family shrine. The purpose of the ceremony was to bring life and health to the land and the people who worked it.

The ancient ceremony of Saturnalia was held at the end of the year. It was held in honor of Saturn, the god of seedtime and harvest. This ceremony took place during the last half of December. The family would go to the temple of Saturn and say prayers to him. Then they would enjoy a feast of food and wine. Freedom was given to the slaves for that festival. In fact, their masters served them! People exchanged gifts and played games.

As the Roman religion matured, more emphasis was placed on the powers of individual gods and goddesses. The most important god was Jupiter, lord of the sky. The Romans thought that he brought light each day, caused the moon to shine and controlled the weather. Lightning was Jupiter's powerful sign, and his symbols were the thunderbolt and eagle.

Juno was Jupiter's wife. She was the queen of the heavens and heavenly light, especially moonlight. Juno was worshiped as the goddess of beginnings of the months and birth. Because her month was June, this was a favorite time for couples to marry.

The greatest festival held in Juno's honor was called Matronalia. It was celebrated by women on the first day of March by the Roman women. Juno was represented as a mother with a flower in one hand and a baby in the other. She was prayed to at her temple and offerings were left for her. When the women returned home from the celebration, they found gifts left for them by their husbands. Juno was also the goddess of marriage.

Another important goddess was Minerva, goddess of wisdom and arts. She was worshiped by craftsmen, artists of every kind, doctors, teachers and school children. Her month was March. On her celebration day, school children were given a holiday and teachers received their yearly pay. This marked the end of one school year and the beginning of a new one.

The next most important god was Mars. He was responsible for fertilizing the fields, protecting animals, and war. His symbols were the wolf, the woodpecker and the lance. It was his son Romulus who is credited with founding Rome.

It was said that Mars fathered twin boys, Romulus and Remus. He protected them while they grew up by sending a she-wolf to look after them. Legend tells us that Romulus and Remus fought over which one had the support of the local gods to rule the new city. Romulus killed his brother, and the city was named Rome after him. Romulus is said to have founded Rome.

There were many gods and goddesses in the pantheon of the ancient Romans. These were the most important.

Jupiter

The Beginning of Roman Mythology

Vocabulary Activities

Look up each word in the dictionary and write its definition.

Pantheon:

Supernatural:

Deities:

Hearth:

Ritual:

Shrine:

Fill in the blanks with a form of the correct vocabulary word from above.

1. The _____ was used to worship Venus.

2. Jupiter was the most important god in the Roman _____.

3. They used a very elaborate _____ to worship the gods.

4. Many thought the gods had _____ powers.

5. The fireplace _____ was made of rocks.

6. All _____ were worshiped in some way.

Use each vocabulary word in a short paragraph about Roman Mythology.

_____

_____

_____

_____

_____

_____

_____

_____

The Beginning of Roman Mythology
Comprehension Questions

1. How did the Greek influence change the initial Roman beliefs about gods and goddesses?

_____

_____

_____

_____

2. Who were the main Roman gods and goddesses?

_____

_____

_____

_____

3. Describe one ceremony that involved the family.

_____

_____

_____

_____

4. Describe Jupiter and his importance.

_____

_____

_____

_____

5. Why was Minerva worshiped by teachers and students?

_____

_____

_____

_____

Answers to "The Beginning of Roman Mythology"
Comprehension Questions and Vocabulary Exercises

Discussion Questions

1. How did the Greek influence change the initial Roman beliefs about gods and goddesses?

In the beginning, the Romans did not give their gods and goddesses human characteristics or shapes. When the Romans conquered the Greeks, the Romans adopted many of the Greek gods and goddesses, giving them Roman names.

2. Who were the most important Roman gods and goddesses?

Jupiter, Juno, Venus, Cupid, Mars, Pluto, Vulcan and Neptune were the principal deities.

3. Describe a ceremony that involved the family. (Two are possible.)

The head of the family placed a small gift in the shrine each day. This was supposed to help the family be successful in work and life. Compitalia was celebrated by farm families. They hung a plough, a wooden doll for each free member of the household, and a woolen ball for every slave in the family shrine. This was supposed to bring life and health to the land and the people.

4. Describe Jupiter and his importance.

Jupiter was king of the gods. He brought light each day and caused the moon to shine. He also controlled the weather. His sign was the lightning bolt and his symbols, the thunderbolt and eagle.

5. Why was Minerva worshiped by teachers and students?

She was the goddess of wisdom. Students were given a holiday and teachers their yearly salary on her celebration day.

Look up each word in the dictionary and write its definition.

Pantheon: all the gods of the religion

Supernatural: relating to phenomena beyond or outside of nature

Deities: divinities, gods or goddesses

Hearth: an area in front of the fireplace (then considered an integral part of the home)

Ritual: an established form for a religious ceremony

Shrine: a place of worship

Fill in the blanks with the correct vocabulary word.

1. The <u>shrine</u> was used to worship Venus.
2. Jupiter was the most important god in the Roman <u>pantheon.</u>
3. They used a very elaborate <u>ritual </u>to worship the gods.
4. Many thought the gods had <u>supernatural</u> powers.
5. The fireplace <u>hearth</u> was made of rocks.
6. All <u>deities</u> were worshiped in some way.

The Beginning of Roman Mythology
Creative-Thinking Questions

1. Analyze why the Romans chose to adopt the Greeks gods and goddesses rather than those of another culture.

_____

_____

_____

_____

2. How do you think the Romans came up with the names of their gods and goddesses? Create a new name for Vesta, goddess of the hearth fire. Tell why you named her such.

_____

_____

_____

_____

3. How might the Romans have explained natural occurrences besides through the actions of gods and goddesses?

_____

_____

_____

_____

4. Why were ceremonies so important to the Romans?

_____

_____

_____

_____

5. Explain why the family was the core of Roman Civilization.

_____

_____

_____

_____

6. What other way might Juno be represented? Explain your answer.

_____

_____

_____

_____

7. Suppose you had been a teacher in the Roman days. Would you like to have been paid once a year? Why or why not?

_____

_____

_____

_____

8. Explain why the wolf, the woodpecker and the lance were the symbols of Mars.

_____

_____

_____

_____

9. Which other month might have been named after a god or goddess? Explain your answer.

_____

_____

_____

_____

The Beginning of Roman Mythology
A SPECIAL INVITATION

Suppose you were invited to Mount Olympus to visit Jupiter
Write about your visit.

The Beginning of Roman Mythology
QUESTIONS FOR JUPITER

Write three questions that you would like to ask Jupiter.
Let a classmate answer your questions and share with the class.

The Beginning of Roman Mythology
A SYMBOL OF POWER

Create a new symbol for Jupiter.
Explain how the new symbol represents his power.

© Educational Impressions, Inc. **15** *Creative Experiences in Roman Mythology*

The Beginning of Roman Mythology
READ ALL ABOUT IT!

Create a new goddess of the moon.
Write about her story.

Spirits of the Underworld

The Romans were concerned about their dead and had special rituals for burying them. These rituals ensured that the soul of the dead made a safe journey from the living world into the world of the Manes. Manes were thought to be the spirits, or souls, of the deceased loved ones.

The dead person's body was washed and dressed in fine clothes. It was then placed on a <u>bier</u> and carried in a family procession to the burial grounds. The roadsides, just outside of town, were usually used for this purpose. Sometimes the dead were buried on their own lands, but not often. Most of the time the body was placed on a <u>pyre</u> and burned. The ashes were gathered and buried. The act of putting the ashes in the ground was most important. The Romans believed that unless it was done correctly, the spirit of the dead would come back and haunt the family, bringing them bad luck.

After the burial, the dead person's house was <u>purified</u> through rituals. The family mourned the loss for five days. Then a sacrifice was given to the family household gods, or Lares.

The wealthy Romans had <u>elaborate</u> funerals. Actors wearing masks paraded along with the funeral procession. The rich usually had very impressive tombs for their dead.

Each February the dead were remembered with a special festival. Graves and tombs were visited and decorated with flowers. Food and drink was left to keep the spirits happy. The Romans believed that if the dead were upset, they might <u>emerge</u> from the grave and haunt the family.

Lares

It was believed that the dead person's soul passed on to the underworld, which was ruled by Pluto and Proserpina. After death, the soul entered the realm beneath the earth. It was ferried across the River Styx by Charon. Charon demanded a small coin from each soul before he would row them to the other side. For this reason a coin was placed on the tongue of every dead person before the funeral.

The entrance to the underworld was guarded by Cerberus, a three-headed dog. The road to the Underworld was divided: one path led to Tartarus, a terrible place of everlasting pain and punishment; the other led to Pluto's palace in Elysium, the land of eternal light. In Elysium those who had lived good lives would enjoy happiness forever.

Spirits of the Underworld
Vocabulary Activities

Look up each word in the dictionary and write its definition.

Bier:

Pyre:

Purify:

Elaborate:

Emerge:

Fill in the blanks with a form of the correct vocabulary word from above.

1. They cleaned the body during the ceremony to _____ it.

2. His spirit will _____ from the grave.

3. The coffin was placed on the _____.

4. The _____ ceremony included many rituals.

5. The _____ burst into flames when torched.

Use the vocabulary words and write a brief paragraph explaining what happens to the dead.

_____

_____

_____

_____

_____

_____

_____

_____

_____

Spirits of the Underworld
Comprehension Questions

1. Describe what the Romans did after a person died.

_____

_____

_____

_____

2. How did the funeral of a rich person differ from that of a poor person?

_____

_____

_____

_____

3. Describe the festival that took place in February. What was the purpose of the festival?

_____

_____

_____

_____

4. Describe the soul's journey to the underworld.

_____

_____

_____

_____

5. Describe the underworld.

_____

_____

_____

_____

Answers to "Spirits of the Underworld" Comprehension Questions and Vocabulary Exercises

Discussion Questions

1. Describe what the Romans did after a person died.

The body was washed and dressed in fine clothes. Then it was placed on a bier and carried to the burial grounds. Usually, the body was burned and the ashes were buried in the ground. The dead person's house was then purified.

2. How did the funeral of a rich person differ from that of a poor person?

The rich would pay actors to wear masks and walk with the funeral procession. They also had very impressive tombs.

3. Describe the festival that took place in February. What was the purpose of the festival?

The dead were visited. Food and drink were left by their graves. The purpose was to keep them happy so they would not come to haunt the family.

4. Describe the soul's journey to the underworld.

The dead person was rowed across the River Styx by Charon. Charon was paid a small coin for his work. The dead would go to either Tartarus or Elysium.

5. Describe the underworld. The underworld was guarded by Cerberus, a three-headed dog. It was divided into two parts: Tartarus, a terrible place of pain and punishment, and Elysium, the land of eternal light.

Look up each word in the dictionary and write its definition.

Bier: a stand bearing a coffin or corpse

Pyre: a combustible heap for burning a dead body as a funeral rite

Purified: the quality or state of being pure

Elaborate: planned or carried out with care and in detail

Emerge: to rise, come forth, come out into view

Fill in the blanks with the correct vocabulary word.

1. They cleaned the body during the ceremony to <u>purify</u> it.
2. His spirit will <u>emerge</u> from the grave.
3. The coffin was placed on the <u>bier</u>.
4. The <u>elaborate</u> ceremony included many rituals.
5. The <u>pyre</u> burst into flames when torched.

Spirits of the Underworld
Creative-Thinking Questions

1. Why, do you think, were the Romans so concerned about their dead?

_____

_____

_____

_____

2. Describe how you think the Manes might have looked.

_____

_____

_____

_____

3. If the family did not bury their dead correctly, they might have been haunted. How would you have haunted your family for not burying you correctly?

_____

_____

_____

_____

4. Suppose your family was poor. How might a funeral of a family member have looked?

_____

_____

_____

_____

5. Your family forgot to put a coin on your tongue when you died. How will you convince Charon to row you across the river?

_____

_____

_____

_____

6. You wish to visit the underworld, but Cerberus will not let you in. Devise a way to trick Cerberus into letting you into the underworld.

_____

_____

_____

_____

7. Judge the roadside as a burial ground for the dead.

_____

_____

_____

_____

8. Suppose your family forgot to give a sacrifice to the family Lares. What might happen?

_____

_____

_____

_____

9. You have been sent to Tartarus. Plan your escape. How will you get out and where will you go?

_____

_____

_____

_____

Spirits of the Underworld
REMEMBER ME!

Suppose you are a rich Roman. Plan your funeral. Describe how you want your tomb to look and how your family should mourn their loss of you.

Spirits of the Underworld
WHO AM I?

You are asked to write an obituary for yourself when you die.
What would you say?

Spirits of the Underworld
RULER FOR A WEEK

Pluto decides to take a vacation and asks you to rule while he is gone.
How will you rule the underworld? Write about it.

Spirits of the Underworld
LAND OF ETERNAL LIGHT

Describe how you think Elysium might look. Write about it.

Cupid and Psyche

Cupid was the god of love, son of Venus and Vulcan. Cupid was <u>portrayed</u> as a winged, fat baby boy. He had a very irresponsible nature.

Cupid always carried a <u>quiver</u> of arrows, which he used to shoot his victims. His gold-tipped arrows caused his victims to fall in love with the first person he or she saw. His lead-tipped arrows, on the other hand, caused his victims to run from love.

Even though Cupid was shown as a winged, fat baby, he was a grown man. Cupid's love story begins with a beautiful young maiden named Psyche. Psyche was the third daughter of a king.

Psyche was a modest girl and did not brag about her beauty. Even so, she was so beautiful that her beauty <u>instigated</u> jealousy in Venus, Cupid's mother and the goddess of love. Venus asked her son to shoot Psyche with one of his gold-tipped arrows and to make her fall in love with a terrible monster. Once Cupid saw Psyche, however, he dropped the arrow meant for her, pricking himself. Cupid immediately fell deeply in love with Psyche.

Psyche consulted the oracle at Delphi and was told that it was in her destiny to marry a monster. When Psyche was told that a marriage had been arranged for her, everyone believed that the groom would be a monster. No one knew that Cupid himself planned to marry her.

Psyche was taken to the top of a mountain, to a remote palace. The two were married, but Cupid had made himself invisible, so neither Psyche nor anyone else could see him. Cupid talked to her lovingly and treated her kindly. His only request was that she never try to look at him. He told her that he would always come at night so that she would not see him.

Every night Cupid visited Psyche. He always behaved kindly and gently toward her. He fulfilled all her heart's desires; nevertheless, Psyche became homesick. She told her husband how lonely she was and convinced him to allow her sisters to visit her.

After seeing Psyche's <u>plush</u> surroundings, her sisters became very jealous. They tried to convince Psyche that her husband was really a monster. They suggested that he was fattening her in order to eat her. They said that the only way for her to live was to kill him.

Her sisters' warnings along with her curiosity encouraged Psyche to go against the wishes and warnings of her husband. That night Psyche took a lamp and knife, ready to kill her monster husband just in case her sisters' suspicions had been correct. The husband she saw, however, was not a monster but a sleeping god—Cupid.

Psyche was immediately filled with remorse. In her surprise, some wax from her candle dripped on Cupid, waking him. He saw Psyche looking at him and immediately disappeared.

Psyche searched and searched for Cupid, but she could not find him. Out of <u>desperation</u>, Psyche went to Venus and asked her for help. Venus was still jealous of Psyche's great beauty, however, and sent her on one quest after another.

Finally, Cupid heard about what Venus was doing. Still in love with Psyche, he went to Jupiter and convinced him to make Venus stop what she was doing. He also convinced him to make Psyche immortal and to help him win the consent of his mother, which he did. Cupid found Psyche and the two were married, living happily ever after.

Cupid and Psyche
Vocabulary Activities

Look up each word in the dictionary and write its definition.

Portrayed:

Quiver:

Instigated:

Plush:

Desperation:

Fill in the blanks with a form of the correct vocabulary word from above.

1. She carried the arrows in a _____ on her shoulder.

2. The _____ surroundings made her feel special.

3. The man was _____ as a hero in the biography.

4. In _____, she cried out for help.

5. The group _____ a riot among the crowd.

Use each of the vocabulary words in a sentence.

Cupid and Psyche
Comprehension Questions

1. Describe Cupid and his duties.

_____

_____

_____

_____

2. Why was Psyche taken to the top of the mountain?

_____

_____

_____

_____

3. Describe Psyche's life on the mountain.

_____

_____

_____

_____

4. Why did Psyche's sisters try and get her to kill her husband?

_____

_____

_____

_____

5. How did the story end?

_____

_____

_____

_____

Answers to "Cupid and Psyche"
Story Discussion Questions and Vocabulary Exercises

Discussion Questions

1. Describe Cupid and his duties.

Cupid was portrayed as a winged, fat baby boy; he was shown to be irresponsible. He was the god of love.

2. Why was Psyche taken to the top of the mountain?

The oracle was consulted and told her that her destiny was to marry a monster. She was taken to the top of the mountain to marry her husband, believed to be a monster.

3. Describe Psyche's life on the mountain.

She was waited on by invisible servants. She lived in a very plush place with everything she needed. Her husband would visit her at night when he could not be seen.

4. Why did Psyche's sisters try and get her to kill her husband?

They were jealous of how well she was being treated.

5. How did the story end?

Cupid and Psyche were finally able to marry and live happily ever after.

Look up each word in the dictionary and write its definition.

Portrayed: depicted; represented

Quiver: a case for carrying arrows

Instigated: provoked, arouse to action or feeling

Plush: very luxurious

Desperation: a loss of hope; surrender to misery or dread

Fill in the blanks with the correct vocabulary word.

1. She carried the arrows in a quiver on her shoulder.

2. The plush surroundings made her feel special.

3. The man was portrayed as a hero in the biography.

4. In desperation, she cried out for help.

5. The group instigated a riot among the crowd.

Cupid and Psyche
Creative-Thinking Questions

1. Cupid was described as irresponsible. What things might he have done for him to be described as such?

_____

_____

_____

_____

2. What thing might have caused Venus to be so jealous of Psyche?

_____

_____

_____

_____

3. Why did Cupid fall in love with Psyche? Do you think it was intentional?

_____

_____

_____

_____

4. Do you think Venus was right to want to punish Psyche?

_____

_____

_____

_____

5. How might the story have been different had Psyche's husband not allowed her sisters to come and visit her?

_____

_____

_____

_____

6. Why, do you suppose, did Cupid disappear when Psyche saw him? Did he have a right to be angry?

_____

_____

_____

_____

7. Suppose Psyche had seen her husband as a monster. What might she have done?

_____

_____

_____

_____

8. Was Venus revengeful? Why or why not?

_____

_____

_____

_____

9. What might Jupiter have said to Venus to help Cupid and Psyche?

_____

_____

_____

_____

Cupid and Psyche
WHAT WOULD HAVE HAPPENED?

How might the story have been different had Cupid carried out Venus' wishes?
Write about it.

Cupid and Psyche
ALL ALONE!

Write about Psyche's feelings as she was alone on the mountain.

Cupid and Psyche
TASKS

Devise several tasks that Psyche must complete in order to find Cupid.

Cupid and Psyche
SO MUCH IN LOVE

Compose a poem about Cupid and Psyche's love.

Pluto, Proserpina, and Ceres

After Jupiter, Neptune and Pluto overthrew their father, Cronus, they drew lots to see which part of the world they would control. Pluto had the worst draw and became lord of the underworld. (In Greek mythology, where the myth originated, Jupiter was called Zeus, Neptune was called Poseidon, and Pluto was known as Hades. In Roman mythology, Pluto is also known as the god of Wealth, because of the great amount of precious metals buried within the earth's depths.)

Pluto spent most of the time in his dark castle in the underworld. His dark personality kept him from being liked by the other gods or mortals. He was not really an evil god; he was stern, unpitying and inexorable, but he was just. Because he ruled the underworld, he was associated with death and feared by men. He wasn't death itself. That was another god, Mors.

Pluto's weapon was the two-pronged fork. He used this to shatter that which got in his way or wasn't to his liking. His other prized possessions included his helmet, which had been given to him by the Cyclops and which made the wearer invisible, and his dark chariot, which was drawn by four coal-black steeds.

Pluto was in love with the beautiful goddess Proserpina (Persephone in Greek mythology). She was the daughter of Jupiter and Ceres (Demeter in Greek mythology), goddess of the harvest. He was determined to have Proserpina as his wife and he left the underworld to get her and bring her to his dark domain.

Ceres loved her daughter greatly and had done her best to shelter her from the ugly things of the world. The two had been living a very peaceful life in the countryside. Ceres spent her time making the land fertile and ripening the golden grains. The people offered her thanks for their wonderful crops. Then one day Proserpina disappeared! She had gone out to pick flowers and did not return.

Ceres and her servants searched the land, but they were unable to find Proserpina. Ceres was devastated by the loss of her daughter. Although at one time she lived in Mount Olympus, she she became so angry that refused to go back. Instead, she roamed the Earth, making the land barren. along the way. She caused the crops to fail. Flowers withered. Blight and disease attacked any plants still alive.

It seemed that mankind would perish from lack of food. The gods were deprived of their sacrifices and gifts. The people prayed to Jupiter. Finally, he agreed to help Ceres. He sent his son Mercury, the messenger god, to Pluto to demand the return of Proserpina. Jupiter also stated that she could only return if she had not eaten any food of the underworld. It was said that anyone eating food of the dead owed allegiance to Pluto, their king.

Because Proserpina had eaten four pomegranate seeds, Pluto refused to let her go. Ceres refused to give up. She told Jupiter that unless her daughter was returned, the earth would again turn barren. The gods knew this would destroy mankind. They came up with a solution, which was accepted by both Pluto and Ceres. For nine months of the year Proserpina would live with her mother; she would spend the remaining three months she as Pluto's bride and queen of the underworld.

For this reason, during the time of the year when Proserpina returns to Pluto, the land becomes barren and cold. When she returns to Ceres in the spring, the earth becomes alive and full of color. Flowers bloom and birds sing their sweet songs. Only when the crops were harvested and the grapes gathered did Proserpina return to her husband, Pluto, to reign by his side as queen of the underworld.

Pluto, Proserpina, and Ceres
Vocabulary Activities

Look up each word in the dictionary and write its definition.

Inexorable:

Barren:

Devastated:

Blight:

Allegiance:

Fill in the blanks with a form of the correct vocabulary word from above.

1. The _____ destroyed the trees.

2. She was _____ by the loss of her pet.

3. The desert was a _____ wasteland.

4. She was _____ about finding the truth.

5. He was awarded by his employer for his _____ to the company.

Use the vocabulary words to write a paragraph about Pluto, Lord of the Underworld.

_____

_____

_____

_____

_____

_____

_____

_____

_____

Pluto, Proserpina, and Ceres
Comprehension Questions

1. Describe how the world was divided among the three gods: Jupiter, Pluto and Neptune.

_____

_____

_____

_____

2. Tell why Pluto was feared by man.

_____

_____

_____

_____

3. What are some of Pluto's character traits?

_____

_____

_____

_____

4. Describe Ceres' job.

_____

_____

_____

_____

5. Tell about the agreement made between Pluto and Ceres regarding Proserpina.

_____

_____

_____

_____

Answers to "Pluto, Proserpina, and Ceres"
Comprehension Questions and Vocabulary Exercises

Discussion Questions

1. Describe how the world was divided among the three gods: Jupiter, Pluto and Neptune.

Jupiter ruled the sky; Poseidon ruled the waters; Pluto ruled the underworld.

2. Tell why Pluto was feared by man.

Pluto was associated with death and darkness, so he was feared by man.

3. What are some of Pluto' character traits?

Pluto was stern, unpitying, inexorable, yet just.

4. Describe Ceres' job.

Ceres was the goddess of harvest; therefore, she made the crops ripen.

5. Tell about the agreement made between Pluto and Ceres regarding Proserpina.

For three months of the year Proserpina would rule beside Pluto in the underworld. The other nine months Proserpina could be found living with her mother. Her absence from Ceres caused winter. Her return brought spring and summer.

Look up each word in the dictionary and write its definition.

Inexorable: relentless

Barren: lifeless

Devastated: reduced to ruin; overwhelmed; overpowered

Blight: plant disease or injury marked by withering

Allegiance: loyalty owed by a citizen to his government

Fill in each sentence with the correct vocabulary word.

1. The <u>blight</u> destroyed the trees.
2. She was <u>devastated</u> by the loss of her pet.
3. The desert was a <u>barren</u> wasteland.
4. She was <u>inexorable</u> about finding the truth.
5. He was awarded by his employer for his <u>allegiance</u> to the company.

Pluto, Proserpina, and Ceres
Creative-Thinking Questions

1. Pluto had a helmet that made him invisible. If you had a helmet that made you invisible, how would you use it?

_____

_____

_____

_____

2. Suppose you were Pluto and unhappy with drawing the underworld as your domain. How might you convince Jupiter or Neptune to change domains with you?

_____

_____

_____

_____

3. How do you think Proserpina felt about being queen of the underworld? Give reasons for your answer.

_____

_____

_____

_____

4. What might mankind have done to persuade Ceres to do her job?

_____

_____

_____

_____

5. If you were Pluto, would you reward someone for having seen Proserpina swallow the seeds? If so, what would the reward be? What would you do if you were Ceres?

_____

_____

_____

_____

6. Was Ceres selfish? Give reasons for your answer.

_____

_____

_____

_____

7. How might the world have been different had Pluto insisted that Proserpina stay with him for nine months and with her mother only three?

_____

_____

_____

_____

8. Suppose Pluto had never taken Proserpina? How might this have effected the world?

_____

_____

_____

_____

Pluto, Lord of the Underworld
A DAY IN THE LIFE OF A QUEEN

Describe a typical day in Proserpina's life as Pluto's queen.

Pluto, Lord of the Underworld
SEASONAL CHANGES

Create another myth to explain the seasons.

Pluto, Lord of the Underworld
INTERVIEW WITH A GOD

Pretend to interview Pluto. Create three question you might like to ask him.
Then answer the questions as Pluto.

Pluto, Lord of the Underworld
DAUGHTER OF CERES CAPTURED

Pretend to be a news reporter.
Write an eyewitness account of how Pluto captured Proserpina.

Apollo and Daphne

Apollo was one of the greatest of all the Olympian Gods. He is the only god whose name is the same in both Greek and Roman mythology. Apollo was known as the god of poetry, music, archery, <u>prophecy</u> and healing. He was <u>depicted</u> as a tall, muscular, youthful god. He was very handsome and had long, slightly curling hair. He was also very charming!

Most of the gods and goddesses of Roman mythology had certain animals as their favorites. Apollo was associated with the wolf; this was curious because he was known as a shepherd who protected flocks of sheep from the wolf. He was also connected to the deer and several species of birds.

In spite of Apollo's handsomeness and charm, he was unlucky in love. He had many true loves, but something always seemed to happen that destroyed his quest for happiness. Such is the story of Apollo and Daphne.

Daphne was a beautiful mountain <u>nymph</u>. She was desired by many, but Apollo was not one of them. Their story begins with Apollo bragging about his superior skills with his bow and arrows. Apollo told everyone that he was better than Cupid, the god of love.

Cupid was determined to <u>retaliate</u>. He took one of his gold-tipped arrows and shot Apollo. This caused Apollo immediately to fall in love with Daphne. Cupid then shot Daphne with one of his lead-tipped arrows, causing her to resist Apollo's advances.

Apollo <u>fervently</u> chased Daphne. She spent as much time running away from him as he did chasing her. This continued for some time until Daphne could no longer stand it.

Finally, Daphne called upon her father Peneus, a river god, to help her. He changed Daphne into a laurel tree. This saddened Apollo so much that he decreed the laurel tree to be his sacred plant. He promised to wear branches from the tree as his crown and to decorate his harp and quiver with it. Apollo also made sure that the tree would always be green and would never lose its leaves so that, like him, the tree would know eternal youth.

Apollo and Daphne
Vocabulary Activities

Look up each word in the dictionary and write its definition.

Prophecy:

Depicted:

Nymph:

Retaliate:

Fervently:

Fill in the blanks with a form of the correct vocabulary word from above.

1. The angry woman promised to _____ for his cruel actions.

2. The old man's _____ was not correct; what he predicted did not occur.

3. She _____ begged her friends for forgiveness.

4. The _____ wore flowers in her hair.

5. The god was _____ in the art book with a spear in his hand.

Write a paragraph about Roman Mythology using the vocabulary words.

_____

_____

_____

_____

_____

_____

_____

Apollo and Daphne
Comprehension Questions

1. Describe Apollo and his duties.

_____

_____

_____

_____

2. What was Apollo's favorite animal and how was it ironic?

_____

_____

_____

_____

3. How did Apollo fall in love with Daphne?

_____

_____

_____

_____

4. Did Daphne return his love?

_____

_____

_____

_____

5. What happened to Daphne?

_____

_____

_____

_____

Answers to "Apollo and Daphne"
Comprehension Questions and Vocabulary Exercises

Discussion Questions

1. Describe Apollo and his duties.

Apollo was tall, muscular and youthful. He was very handsome and had long, slightly curling hair. He was also very charming! Apollo was the god of poetry, music, archery, prophecy and healing.

2. What was Apollo's favorite animal and why was it ironic?

Apollo's favorite animal was the wolf. It was ironic because he was known as a shepherd who protected flocks of sheep from wolves.

3. Why did Apollo fall in love with Daphne?

Cupid shot him with a gold-tipped arrow, making him fall in love with her.

4. Did Daphne return his love? Explain your answer.

No, he did not. Cupid shot her with a lead-tipped arrow; this made her want to resist Apollo.

5. What happened to Daphne?

She was turned into a laurel tree.

Look up each word in the dictionary and write its definition

Prophecy: a foretelling of the future

Depicted: represented by a picture

Nymph: one of the many goddesses in old legends represented as beautiful young girls living in mountains, forests, meadows, and waters

Retaliate: to return in kind; to get revenge

Fervently: with great depth of feeling

Fill in the blanks with the correct vocabulary word.

1. The angry woman promised to <u>retaliate</u> for his cruel actions.

2. The old man's <u>prophecy</u> was not correct; what he predicted did not occur.

3. She <u>fervently</u> begged her friends for forgiveness.

4. The <u>nymph</u> wore flowers in her hair.

5. The god was <u>depicted</u> in the art book with a spear in his hand.

Apollo and Daphne
Creative-Thinking Questions

1. Apollo was the god of prophecy. Why, do you suppose, did he fail to see what was going to happen to him and Daphne?

_____

_____

_____

_____

2. Why, do you think, did Apollo choose a wolf as his favorite animal?

_____

_____

_____

_____

3. Do you think Daphne might have fallen in love with Apollo under different circumstances? Why or why not?

_____

_____

_____

_____

4. What other way might Cupid have gotten revenge for Apollo's bragging?

_____

_____

_____

_____

5. If you had been Apollo, how might you have convinced Daphne to accept your love?

_____

_____

_____

_____

6. What other way might Peneus have helped Daphne besides turning her into a laurel tree?

_____

_____

_____

_____

7. Was Cupid's revenge fair? Why or why not?

_____

_____

_____

_____

8. Create a way to reverse Cupid's damage.

_____

_____

_____

_____

9. How might Apollo have changed Daphne back into herself?

_____

_____

_____

_____

Apollo and Daphne
OUR LIFE TOGETHER

Suppose Apollo and Daphne had gotten together. Write about their life.

Apollo and Daphne
I'M OUT OF HERE!

Create a way for Daphne to escape Apollo without hurting his feelings.
Write about it.

Apollo and Daphne
REVENGE

Devise a way for Apollo to get back at Cupid for his lost love.

Apollo and Daphne
YOU CALL THIS A LIFE!

How do you think Daphne's life changed as a laurel tree?
Write about it.

Diana and Actaeon

Diana, the goddess of the hunt, was very beautiful. In Greek mythology she was known as Artemis. Diana loved nature. She lived in the forest with her wood nymphs.

Her palace was a cave in the side of a hill. She decorated it with an arched roof made of stones, delicately fitted with such precision that it looked as smooth as glass. A fountain burst from one side of the cave into a basin which she used for bathing.

One day, in the woods near the cave where Diana lived, a hunter named Actaeon and his friends were hunting stags. They grew tired and decided that it was time to indulge in a restful evening. Actaeon left his friends and searched for a nice soft place to lie down and rest for the night.

That same day, after a long day of hunting, Diana came into her cave and handed her javelin, her quiver and her bow to one of her nymphs. She took off her robe and sandals, as he prepared for a nice hot bath. Just as she let herself down into the basin, a man appeared at the cave entrance. That man was Actaeon, son of King Cadmus.

Upon his appearance, the nymphs tried to cover Diana's body with theirs. They screamed at the sight of a man. Diana reached for her bow and arrows, but they had been placed away from her in preparation of her bath. She looked at the intruder and murmured these words, "Now go and tell, if you can, that you have seen Diana unapparelled."

Immediately a pair of stag's horns grew from Actaeon's head. His neck gained length and his ears grew sharp-pointed. His hands became feet; his arms became long legs; and his body soon was covered with a hairy spotted hide.

Actaeon's boldness was replaced by fear. He fled the cave, astounded by his newly acquired speed. As he ran past a pond, he glanced down and saw the pair of horns growing from his head. He tried to scream, but nothing came from his mouth. He groaned, and tears flowed down the face that had taken the place of his own.

Actaeon decided to run into the woods and hide. As he ran by his old camp, the dogs that had helped him hunt and kill the stags that day, caught his scent. Immediately they began to bark. The barking signaled to his friends that there was a stag nearby. Actaeon's friends turned the dogs loose, unaware that the stag was in reality their friend.

Actaeon moved more swiftly than the wind, jumping over gorges and climbing up rocks, but try as he might, he could not outrun his own dogs. He tried to shout at them, but nothing would come from his mouth. The fastest dog jumped on Actaeon's back and began to tear at him. One by one the dogs caught up with him and jumped at him. They grabbed his legs, his shoulders—whatever they could sink their sharp teeth into—and attacked the master whom they no longer recognized.

Soon Actaeon was pulled to the ground. He could hear his friends cheer the dogs on as he himself had done earlier that day. His friends were calling his name so that he, too, could join in the sport, but he was not to be found. His life was being torn from him so that Diana's anger could be satisfied.

Diana and Actaeon
Vocabulary Activities

Look up each word in the dictionary and write its definition.

Precision:

Indulge

Basin:

Intruder:

Astounded:

Fill in the blanks with a form of the correct vocabulary word from above.

1. She liked to _____ in a bubble bath after a day at work.

2. His watch was a _____ instrument.

3. He was _____ by what the precocious child said.

4. The cliff _____ was full of water.

5. She called the police because a(n) _____ had been in the house.

Match to vocabulary word to its synonym.

_____ 1. Precision   A. Bowl

_____ 2. Basin   B. Surprised

_____ 3. Intruder   C. Pamper

_____ 4. Indulge   D. Trespasser

_____ 5. Astounded   E. Exactness

Diana and Actaeon
Comprehension Questions

1. Describe Diana's home.

_____

_____

_____

_____

2. How did Actaeon and Diana meet?

_____

_____

_____

_____

3. What was Diana's punishment for Actaeon?

_____

_____

_____

_____

4. Describe Actaeon's feelings towards his new body.

_____

_____

_____

_____

5. What happened to Actaeon in the end?

_____

_____

_____

_____

Answers to "Diana and Actaeon"
Comprehension Questions and Vocabulary Exercises

Discussion Questions

1. Describe Diana's home.

She lived in a cave in the forest. The roof was of arched stones. A fountain provided a place for her to bathe.

2. How did Actaeon and Diana meet?

Actaeon was looking for a place to rest and stumbled into Diana's cave just as she was about to enter her bath.

3. What was Diana's punishment for Actaeon?

She turned him into a stag.

4. Describe Actaeon's feelings towards his new body.

He was astounded by his increased speed, but shocked by his appearance.

5. What happened to Actaeon in the end?

He was killed by his own hunting hounds.

Look up each word in the dictionary and write its definition.

Precision: exactness; perfection

Indulge: to give in to one's own or another's desires

Basin: a hollow area or enclosure containing water

Intruder: a trespasser; one who enters without being welcome

Astounded: filled with puzzled wonder

Fill in the correct word for each sentence.

1. She liked to <u>indulge</u> in a bubble bath after a day at work.
2. His watch was a <u>precision</u> instrument.
3. He was <u>astounded</u> by what the precocious child said.
4. The cliff <u>basin</u> was full of water.
5. She called the police because an <u>intruder</u> had been in the house.

Match the vocabulary word to its synonym.

_E_	1. Precision	A. Bowl
_A_	2. Basin	B. Surprised
_D_	3. Intruder	C. Pamper
_C_	4. Indulge	D. Trespasser
_B_	5. Astounded	E. Exactness

Diana and Actaeon
Creative-Thinking Questions

1. Suppose Actaeon had not stumbled into Diana's cave. How might the story have been different?

_____

_____

_____

_____

2. From the story, describe Diana's personality.

_____

_____

_____

_____

3. Why, do you suppose, were the nymphs so afraid of a man?

_____

_____

_____

_____

4. What other animal might Diana have changed Actaeon into and why?

_____

_____

_____

_____

5. Suppose you had been Actaeon and saw the changes taking place in your body. How would you have reacted?

_____

_____

_____

_____

6. What was the irony of the story?

_____

_____

_____

_____

7. How do you think Actaeon's friends felt when they learned what had happened?

_____

_____

_____

_____

8. Was it right for Diana to punish Actaeon so severely? Why or why not?

_____

_____

_____

_____

9. What might Diana do differently to keep another man from entering her home?

_____

_____

_____

_____

Diana and Actaeon
A CHANGE OF SCENERY!

Create a new home for Diana taking into consideration where she enjoys living.
Illustrate a picture of the new home and write a descriptive paragraph about it.

Diana and Actaeon
FROM ANOTHER POINT OF VIEW

Pretend to be one of Diana's nymphs. Write a detail description of the incident.

Diana and Actaeon
BAD NEWS...

Write about Actaeon's friends' account of the incident
when they explain to his father what happened to him.

Diana and Actaeon
IN HIS MEMORY

Create a poem in memory of Actaeon.

Venus and Adonis

Originally Venus was the Roman goddess of springtime, crop <u>cultivation</u> and gardens. Eventually, the Romans changed Venus to the goddess of love and beauty—the equivalent of the Greek goddess Aphrodite. Her name stands for desire, charm and grace. It was said that Venus was desired by all men, including Jupiter. This made Juno very jealous so she gave Venus to Vulcan as his wife.

Vulcan was the god of fire and, therefore, the <u>forge</u>. Because the people believed that smoke from volcanoes came from his forge, Vulcan was also associated with volcanoes. In fact, his workshop was thought to be under a volcano. As the "smith god," Vulcan made special tools and weapons for the gods. With the help of the Cyclopes, he even forged the thunderbolts for Jupiter.

Vulcan was ugly and deformed. When the marriage between Venus and Vulcan was announced, everyone watched Venus to see how she would react. They were surprised at her calm demeanor. She smiled because she knew she could control Vulcan.

Venus and Vulcan's marriage brought about a boy child named Cupid. Cupid was the god of love. He had two sets of arrows: gold-tipped arrows, which caused his victims to fall in love with the first person he or she saw, and lead-tipped arrows, which caused his victims to reject love. One day Cupid and his mother were playing when one of Cupid's arrows accidentally wounded Venus. The wound was deep. Before it could heal, Venus saw Adonis, a mortal.

Under the spell of her son's arrow, Venus immediately fell in love with Adonis. She was completely <u>captivated</u> by him. She lost interest in all her normal activities. She no longer enjoyed relaxing in the shade of the trees as had been her habit. She even <u>abstained</u> from going to Olympus.

Instead, Venus followed Adonis everywhere. Dressing like the huntress Diana, she ran through the forests with Adonis, hunting hares, stags and other safe game. She stayed away from the more dangerous game, however, and warned Adonis to do the same. One day she gave her usual warning to stay clear of dangerous creatures such as bears, wolves and boars. Then she got into her swan-drawn chariot and flew into the air.

Adonis was a thrill seeker and did not <u>heed</u> her warning. When his dogs chased a wild boar out of the brush, Adonis threw his spear at the animal, wounding it. This enraged the animal. The boar withdrew the spear with his jaws and rushed towards Adonis, who took off running. The boar caught Adonis and buried his teeth deep in his side. It left him to die.

Venus heard her love's groan and came quickly to his side. She could see his lifeless body covered with blood. Venus wept. As she cried, she beat her chest and pulled her hair. As a memorial of her grief she turned the blood of Adonis into an Anemone, or windflower. Just as the wind causes its blood-red blossoms to open so does it blow the petals away—just as Adonis was taken away from Venus. Although the Anemone is short lived, however, it is a perennial—an annual reminder of her love.

Venus and Adonis
Vocabulary Activities

Look up each word in the dictionary and write its definition.

Cultivation:

Forge:

Captivated:

Abstained:

Heed:

Fill in the blanks with a form of the correct vocabulary word from above.

1. She _____ from eating dessert for a month to try to loose weight.

2. The blacksmith had a giant _____.

3. The _____ of the crops usually took place in the spring.

4. Her father told her to _____ his warning, but she did not obey.

5. The girl was _____ by his charm and good looks.

Write an original sentence using each of the vocabulary words.

_____

_____

_____

_____

_____

_____

_____

_____

_____

Venus and Adonis
Comprehension Questions

1.What were Venus's jobs as a goddess?

_____

_____

_____

_____

2. Describe Vulcan and his job.

_____

_____

_____

_____

3. Why did Venus fall in love with Adonis?

_____

_____

_____

_____

4. How did Venus's relationship with Adonis change her?

_____

_____

_____

_____

5. Describe the death of Adonis.

_____

_____

_____

_____

Answers to "Venus and Adonis"
Comprehension Questions and Vocabulary Exercises

Discussion Questions

1. What were Venus's jobs as a goddess?

At first she was the goddess of springtime, crops, cultivation and gardens. Later, when she began to be associated with the Greek Aphrodite, she became the goddess of love.

2. Describe Vulcan and his job.

Vulcan was ugly and deformed. He was the god of fire and as such was also the god of the forge and the god of volcanoes. He made the special tools and weapons for the gods.

3. Why did Venus fall in love with Adonis?

One of Cupid's arrows wounded her. Adonis was the first man she saw; therefore. under the spell of the arrow, she fell in love with him.

4. How did her relationship with Adonis change her?

She lost interest in all but Adonis. She no longer enjoyed relaxing in the shade. Instead she followed Adonis wherever he went and hunted with him.

5. Describe Adonis' death.

Against Venus's advice, he threw his spear at a wild boar. The boar attacked him with his tusks and killed him.

Look up each word's definition in the dictionary.

Cultivation: to prepare land for the raising of crops

Forge: a furnace or a shop with its furnace where metal is shaped and worked by heating and hammering

Captivated: to influence or fascinate by some special charm

Abstained: kept oneself from doing something

Heed: to pay attention to

Fill in the blanks with the correct vocabulary word.

1. She <u>abstained</u> from eating dessert for a month to try to loose weight.
2. The blacksmith had a giant <u>forge</u>.
3. The <u>cultivation</u> of the crops usually took place in the spring.
4. Her father told her to <u>heed</u> his warning, but she did not obey.
5. The girl was <u>captivated</u> by his charm and good looks.

Venus and Adonis
Creative-Thinking Questions

1. Was Juno's revenge on Venus fair? Why or why not?

_____

_____

_____

_____

2. Suppose you had been Venus and given to Vulcan. How might you have felt?

_____

_____

_____

_____

3. Do you think Vulcan was happy about having Venus as a wife? Why or why not?

_____

_____

_____

_____

4. How might Cupid have kept his mother from falling in love with Adonis after her wound?

_____

_____

_____

_____

5. Why, do you suppose, did Adonis fail to heed Venus's warnings?

_____

_____

_____

_____

6. What do you think Venus might have done to the boar had she found it? Would that be fair? Explain your answer.

_____

_____

_____

_____

7. What might Adonis have done to get away from the boar?

_____

_____

_____

_____

8. Venus turned the body of Adonis into a flower as a memorial. What might you have done instead of turning him into a flower? Why?

_____

_____

_____

_____

9. If you could pick any flower to use as a memorial to a loved one, what flower would you choose and why?

_____

_____

_____

_____

Venus and Adonis
A DAY IN THEIR LIFE

Write about a typical day in the life of Venus and Adonis
on one of their hunting ventures.

Venus and Adonis
HAPPILY EVER AFTER?

How might the story have been different had Adonis not been killed?
Write about it.

Venus and Adonis
CAUGHT IN THE TRAP

Devise a trap to catch the wild boar.
Illustrate your idea and write a description of the trap.

Venus and Adonis
WHAT A PAIR!

Suppose it had been Jupiter whom Venus first saw after being wounded with
Cupid's arrow. How might the story have been different? Write about it.

Mars and His Sons, the Mythical Founders of Rome

Mars was one of the most important gods in the Roman pantheon and was probably the most widely worshiped. He was the son of Jupiter and Juno. In the beginning of Roman history, Mars was the god of spring, vegetation, and fertility. He was also the protector of cattle. As the empire expanded, Mars began to be identified with the Greek god Ares. It was then that Mars began to be thought of as the god of war. With the growth of the empire, the worship of Mars also grew.

Mars was portrayed as a warrior in full battle armor. He wore a crested helmet and carried a shield. His sacred animals were the wolf and woodpecker. The month of March was named after him. Many wars were started in the spring because it was the month of this important god of war.

In ancient times the Romans thought of themselves as the descendants of Mars. That was because, according to the legend, Rome was founded by his sons. Indeed the city was named for one of them.

Mars had twin sons by Rhea Silvia. Amulius, who had overthrown the twins' grandfather as king Alba Longa, feared that one of the twins would someday overthrow him. He had the boys and their mother placed in a trough and cast into the River Tiber. The god Tiberinus saved Rhea Silvia from drowning. The brothers were rescued by a she-wolf who had been sent to them from Mars. The boys were reared with her cubs underneath a fig tree. A few years later, a shepherd took the boys home and gave them to his wife to raise. The shepherd and his wife named the boys Romulus and Remus.

Once Romulus and Remus reached maturity, Mars became involved in his sons' rearing. He taught them how to be great warriors. They killed Amulius, who had tried to drown them, and gave back the kingdom to their grandfather.

The twins planned to build a great city. They began by building a settlement on the Palatine Hill—the place where the she-wolf had raised them. Before long, however, the two began to argue over many things, including which one of them would be king. Each claimed to have the support of the local gods to rule the new city and to give the new city his name. During one dispute about the height of the walls Romulus was having built, Romulus slew Remus. The matter was settled. Romulus continued with the building and named the new city Roma (Rome).

In founding the great city of Rome, Romulus also created the Roman Legions and the Senate. He populated the city with outlaws and fugitives. There were not enough wives for these men, however. Therefore, he <u>abducted</u> the women of the neighboring Sabine tribes. He had tricked them into coming by inviting them to a great festival.

Romulus became a great conqueror, adding great numbers of people and lands to the <u>dominion</u> of Rome. After his death, Romulus was worshiped as the god Quirinus and was believed to have joined his father on Mount Olympus.

Mars and His Sons
Vocabulary Activities

Look up each word in the dictionary and write its definition.

Founded

Shepherd:

Dispute:

Abducted:

Dominion:

Fill in the blanks with a form of the correct vocabulary word from above.

1. St. Augustine, Florida, was _____ in 1565 by the Spaniards.

2. The _____ looked after his sheep with great care.

3. The king's _____ included the surrounding countryside.

4. Their _____ was over who was the rightful owner of the land.

5. The kidnapper _____ the man and held him for ransom.

Use the vocabulary words to write a paragraph about the beginning of Rome.

_____

_____

_____

_____

_____

_____

_____

_____

_____

Mars and His Sons
Comprehension Questions

1. Explain why Mars was so important.

_____

_____

_____

_____

2. How was Mars portrayed?

_____

_____

_____

_____

3. Why was he associated with the founding of Rome?

_____

_____

_____

_____

4. How did Romulus get more citizens for Rome?

_____

_____

_____

_____

5. What happened to Romulus after his death?

_____

_____

_____

_____

Answers to "Mars and His Sons"
Comprehension Questions and Vocabulary Exercises

Discussion Questions

1. Explain why Mars was so important.

Rome was agricultural and Mars was the god of vegetation and fertility and the protector of cattle. He was later the god of war. This may have been because when the empire grew and there was war, the fields also needed protection.

2. How was Mars portrayed?

He was shown as a warrior in full battle armor, wearing a crested helmet and carrying a shield.

3. Why was he associated with the founding of Rome?

One of his sons, Romulus, is the mythical founder of Rome.

4. How did Romulus get more citizens for Rome?

He abducted women from neighboring countries.

5. What happened to Romulus after his death?

He was made into the god Quirinus and lived on Mount Olympus.

Look up each of the vocabulary words in the dictionary and write their definitions.

Founded: established

Shepherd: a person who takes care of sheep

Dispute: an argument; a disagreement

Abducted: carried off by force

Dominion: territory of influence; realm

Fill in the blank with the correct vocabulary word.

1. St. Augustine, Florida, was <u>founded</u> in 1565 by the Spaniards.

2. The <u>shepherd</u> looked after his sheep with great care.

3. The king's <u>dominion</u> included the surrounding countryside.

4. Their <u>dispute</u> was over who was the rightful owner of the land.

5. 5. The kidnapper <u>abducted</u> the man and held him for ransom.

Mars and His Sons
Creative-Thinking Questions

1. Analyze why Mars evolved into the god of war.

_____

_____

_____

_____

2. What other symbol might you choose for Mars and why?

_____

_____

_____

_____

3. Why were the twins and their mother thrown into the river?

_____

_____

_____

_____

4. What might have happened had the twin sons of Mars not been saved?

_____

_____

_____

_____

5. What kind of man do you think Romulus was? Why? Judge the fact that he abducted the Sabine women.

_____

_____

_____

_____

6. Suppose Remus had become Rome's founder. How might things have been different?

_____

_____

_____

_____

7. Would you have made Romulus a god? Why or why not?

_____

_____

_____

_____

8. Do you think Mars was proud of his sons? Why or why not?

_____

_____

_____

_____

9. How do you think it would be to be raised by a wolf? Explain your answer.

_____

_____

_____

_____

Mars and His Sons
REMUS HAS DIED

Write a newspaper report about the death of Remus.

Mars and His Sons
A DAY IN THE LIFE OF ROMULUS AND REMUS

Describe the rearing of Mars's twin sons in a diary.

Mars and His Sons
ROME IN THE BEGINNING

Draw a picture of how you think Rome might have looked in the beginning.

Mars and His Sons
A DEBATE

Prepare a debate.
You must defend either Romulus or Remus as the ruler of Rome.
Get a classmate to defend the other twin and debate the issue.

Bellerophone and Pegasus

Bellerophone was another young Roman. He was brave and courageous, always willing to accept any challenge. What he really wanted to be deemed a hero.

One day, Bellerophone was given a <u>daunting</u> challenge. The king of Lycia challenged Bellerophone to kill the Chimaera, a <u>ferocious</u> monster. The Chimaera had the body of a goat, the head of a great lion and the tail of a serpent. It spewed flames from its mouth. The flames were so hot that they would roast anything or anyone that got close to it.

The Chimaera roamed the countryside, killing villagers and burning their villages. This upset the king not only because he lost his subjects but also because he lost the grain fields that fed his kingdom.

Bellerophone thought about the challenge and finally accepted it. He felt <u>overwhelmed</u> as he tried to figure out how to kill the Chimaera. Bellerophone dropped to his knees and prayed to Minerva for wisdom. Minerva heard his prayers. Because she knew that Bellerophone wanted to help the king and wasn't trying to defeat the Chimaera for his own glory, she decided to come to his aid.

Minerva sent Bellerophone her winged horse, Pegasus. Pegasus was said to have come from Medusa's blood when Perseus cut off her head. Pegasus was the most powerful horse in the world. His swift movements unseated many riders. Minerva tamed Pegasus and had no fear of him, but most others dared not mount him.

Bellerophone jumped onto Pegasus' back and away he flew towards the Chimaera. He <u>soared</u> about Lycia, searching for the dreaded monster. At the same time both Bellerophone and Pegasus spotted the monster as it burned a village.

Pegasus swooped down towards the Chimaera. The Chimaera saw them and turned, unleashing his fearsome flames on the them. The two heroes—man and horse—stayed just out of the reach of the Chimaera's burning-hot flames.

The Chimaera swung his spiked serpent's tail towards the two, trying to knock them from the sky. He was not successful. Pegasus and Bellerophone could not be moved. They showed no fear of the great monster.

Bellerophone took his bow and placed an arrow in it. Pegasus hovered just above the head of the Chimaera. He remaining steady as Bellerophone let the arrow fly, piercing the Chimaera's neck. Bellerophone shot one after another until the monster finally fell to the ground, destroyed.

Bellerophone, still on Pegasus' back, flew back to the kingdom. He announced that he had destroyed the dreaded Chimaera. Everyone was astonished and celebrated the hero's return. The king rewarded Bellerophone with his daughter's hand in marriage. However, Bellerophone was not satisfied. Now that he had accomplished such a <u>monumental</u> task, he considered himself to be immortal. He wanted to join the gods.

Bellerophone guided Pegasus towards the heavens. Jupiter glanced down and saw the approaching mortal on the winged horse. The sight angered him. Mortals were not supposed to approach the gods' domain.

Jupiter threw a thunderbolt, hitting Bellerophone. Pegasus continued his flight towards the heavens, but Bellerophone fell to the earth. He wandered from land to land for the rest of his life until he finally died. Pegasus, on the other hand, was allowed to fly into the heavens. He can still be seen there today.

Bellerophone and Pegasus
Vocabulary Activities

Look up each word in the dictionary and write its definition.

Daunting:

Ferocious:

Overwhelmed:

Soared:

Monumental:

Fill in the blanks with a form of the correct vocabulary word from above.

1. The ruler's _____ stretched for miles.

2. She was _____ with all the work and asked for help.

3. The animal was _____ when cornered.

4. The kite _____ as the child ran across the field.

5. The _____ job seemed impossible until he broke it into small parts.

Use each word in a paragraph and tell about Bellerophone.

_____

_____

_____

_____

_____

_____

_____

_____

_____

Bellerophone and Pegasus
Comprehension Questions

1. Describe the Chimaera.

_____

_____

_____

_____

2. Whom did Bellerophone pray to and how was he helped?

_____

_____

_____

_____

3. Explain how the Chimaera was destroyed.

_____

_____

_____

_____

4. Why was Jupiter upset with Bellerophone?

_____

_____

_____

5. How did Jupiter teach Bellerophone a lesson?

_____

_____

_____

Answers to "Bellerophone and Pegasus"
Comprehension Questions and Vocabulary Exercises

Discussion Questions

1. Describe the Chimaera.

The Chimaera had the body of a goat, the head of a great lion and the tail of a serpent. It spewed flames from its mouth.

2. Whom did Bellerophone pray to and how was he helped?

He prayed to Minerva and she sent him her winged horse, Pegasus.

3. Explain how the Chimaera was destroyed.

Bellerophone and Pegasus flew above his head. Bellerophone shot arrows into him until he died.

4. Why was Jupiter upset with Bellerophone?

Bellerophone thought that because he had slain the Chimaera, he should be able to live on Mount Olympus with the gods. This made Jupiter angry.

5. How did Jupiter teach Bellerophone a lesson?

Jupiter knocked Bellerophone to earth with a thunderbolt. Bellerophone then wandered the earth for the rest of his life, eventually dying a homeless man.

Look up each word in the dictionary and write its definition.

Daunting: discouraging through fear

Ferocious: fierce, savage

Overwhelmed: overcome completely; presented with an excessive amount

Soared: rose high; flew upward

Monumental: massive, outstanding

Fill in the blanks with the correct vocabulary word.

1. The ruler's <u>domain</u> stretched for miles.
2. She was <u>overwhelmed</u> with all the work and asked for help.
3. The animal was <u>ferocious</u> when cornered.
4. The kite <u>soared</u> as the child ran across the field.
5. The <u>monumental</u> job seemed impossible until he broke it into small parts.

Bellerophone and Pegasus
Creative-Thinking Questions

1. What might have happened had Bellerophone not accepted the king's challenge?

_____

_____

_____

_____

2. What other god or goddess might Bellerophone have prayed to for help? Why?

_____

_____

_____

_____

3. What might have happened had the Chimaera not been destroyed?

_____

_____

_____

_____

4. Explain how Pegasus might have sprung from Medusa's blood.

_____

_____

_____

_____

5. Suppose the Chimaera had hit Pegasus with his spiked tail. How might that have changed the myth?

_____

_____

_____

_____

6. What other weapon could Bellerophone have used to destroy the Chimaera? Explain why you chose that weapon.

_____

_____

_____

_____

7. Do you think the Chimaera would be easy to kill? Why or why not?

_____

_____

_____

_____

8. Should Bellerophone have been allowed to live on Mount Olympus? Why or why not?

_____

_____

_____

_____

9. What other way might Jupiter have punished Bellerophone?

_____

_____

_____

_____

Bellerophone and Pegasus
AN EYE-WITNESS ACCOUNT

Write an eye witness account of the battle between Bellerophone and the Chimaera. Use descriptive words to make the battle interesting.

Bellerophone and Pegasus
MY HERO

Plan a way to help Bellerophone keep his hero status after Jupiter's punishment.

Bellerophone and Pegasus

ANOTHER POINT OF VIEW

Write about the battle from the Chimaera's point of view.

Bellerophone and Pegasus
ANOTHER CHALLENGE

Create another challenge for Bellerophone
that would assure him a place on Mount Olympus.

The Story of Aeneas

The story of Aeneas, based on an epic poem by the poet Virgil, follows the Trojan hero Aeneas through a journey to start a new civilization after the fall of Troy. Aeneas was the son of Anchises, King of Dardanians, and the goddess Venus. Venus helped Aeneas throughout the long journey, protecting him from Juno, who wished to see him destroyed.

Aeneas, his children, his father and a few followers had escaped from the burning city of Troy, which had been destroyed by the Greeks. The group made their way to the coast of Phyrgia. They built a fleet of ships and set off to find a new home.

Their first stop was the land of the Harpies. The Harpies were grim monsters with wings, talons, and bodies of ferocious birds, but faces of women. The travelers were tired and hungry. When they saw a large herd of cattle, they killed a few to cook and eat.

This brought about the Harpies' <u>vengeance</u>. The Harpies swooped down and grabbed the travelers' food with their talons. Everything the Harpies touched turned <u>foul</u>. Then the Harpies' leader flew close and made a prophecy: "How dare you come to our island, raiding our cattle and attacking us with your swords! For this wrong you shall be punished! Yes, you will arrive in Italy—that is your destiny—but you shall not make your home there until a terrible hunger has forced you to eat your own tables."

Her prophecy left Aeneas and his followers feeling <u>despondent</u>. It seemed as though their troubles would never end. Aeneas and the others offered prayers to the gods. They begged for their help and guidance for the rest of their journey.

A while later they arrived in Buthrotum. They spent several months there with Helenus, who was a prophet. He told the travelers that their final destination would, in fact, be Italy. He warned them, however, that they would encounter many dangers before finally reaching Italy. He advised him to offer sacrifices to Juno in order to appease her.

Juno did her evil work by blowing their ships far out to sea where they would have to overcome perils such as a one-eyed Cyclopes; a whirlpool; and Scylla, the six-headed monster. With the help of Venus the group survived Juno's anger so they could continue their journey.

As the group approached the end of their journey, Juno became furious at their success, so she devised a plan to stop them. She called upon the Aeolus, god of the winds, to sink the Trojan fleet. Aeolus unleashed his winds, battering the ships. Spars snapped and many valiant Trojan crewmen were lost.

Neptune, the sea god, saw what was happening and quickly came to their rescue. He calmed the waves and sent the winds away. He warned Aeolus not to meddle in the Trojans' affairs again. Aeolus heeded his warning.

The group anchored in a cove. They went ashore and prepared a meal from their <u>meager</u> provisions. Aeneas climbed to the top of a hill. From there he saw a herd of deer grazing quietly. Sent by Venus, the deer provided enough meat for a feast.

The Trojans needed provisions and explored the countryside, looking for a place to obtain their supplies. They came upon the city of Carthage. Dido, the queen of Carthage had been ordered by a messenger of Jupiter to welcome the Trojans and to give them what they needed.

Juno saw another chance to stop Aeneas. She sent Cupid to cause the queen and Aeneas fall in love so that Aeneas would stay in Carthage. Juno did not want the Trojans to succeed because of a prophecy that had been made by Jupiter. He had prophesied that Aeneas would build his city in Italy and conquer many people. He said that Ascanius, son of Aeneas, would be king for many years and that Ascanius would establish a new city called Alba Longa. The prophecy also said that kings would rule there until twin sons were born to Mars and a royal priestess. Jupiter predicted that one of the boys would build a great city and that the people of that city would rule the world. Because Juno favored the Greek people, she did not want the Trojans to become great.

Juno's plan seemed to work until a messenger from Jupiter told Aeneas to leave Carthage and get on with his journey. Aeneas told the news to Dido. She became so distraught that she killed herself. Aeneas was upset, but he did not dare to disobey the gods. He and his group set out for the last part of their journey.

Aeneas and his fellow Trojans finally arrived at their destination. There they lived very modestly on the provisions they had left. One day they sat down to a meal of flat cakes piled with fruit. After eating the fruit, they were still hungry and began to eat the flat cakes. "Look, we are eating the tables, too," Ascanius cried out, reminding them of the Harpy's prediction.

A nearby kingdom was ruled by a king who had a beautiful daughter named Lavinia. Although she had been promised to Turnus, King of Rutulians, a <u>soothsayer</u> told Lavinia's father that she would not marry Turnus. He went on to say that strangers would make the city their stronghold and that Lavinia was destined to marry the leader of their group.

News of this prophecy traveled to Turnus, and he became furious. He set out to wage war against Aeneas. The war went on for several years until Aeneas, with the help of Venus, conquered Turnus. Aeneas married Lavinia, fulfilling the prophecy and joining two nations. His people built an impressive city, which he named Lavinium. Aeneas lived out his days in happiness, watching his son Ascanius grow to manhood and take over the kingdom to fulfill still another prophecy.

When Aeneas died, Venus went to Jupiter and asked him to make her son immortal. Jupiter consented to her wishes. Venus used her divine powers and made Aeneas a god. People built a temple in his honor and he was known as Jupiter Indiges.

Ascanius left Lavinium after his father's death and founded a new settlement in the hills. It was called Alba. Here his descendants ruled for the next four hundred years.

The Story of Aeneas
Vocabulary Activities

Look up each word in the dictionary and write its definition.

Vengeance:

Foul:

Despondent:

Meager:

Soothsayer:

Fill in the blank with the correct vocabulary word.

1. The _____ meal was not enough for one person, let alone four.

2. The predictions of the _____ seemed to come true.

3. The _____ odor was bad enough to make everyone leave the party.

4. The king wanted to get even; his _____ put fear in everyone.

5. She was _____ after he left because she missed him so much.

Match the vocabulary word to its antonym.

_____ 1. Vengeance   A. Plentiful

_____ 2. Foul   B. Truce

_____ 3. Despondent   C. Historian

_____ 4. Meager   D. Pleasant

_____ 5. Soothsayer   E. Happy

The Story of Aeneas
Comprehension Questions

1. Why did Aeneas leave Troy?

_____

_____

_____

_____

2. Describe the Harpies and their anger towards Aeneas and his followers.

_____

_____

_____

_____

3. What was Jupiter's prediction for Aeneas?

_____

_____

_____

_____

4. Why did Dido kill herself?

_____

_____

_____

_____

5. How did the Harpies' prophecy come true?

_____

_____

_____

_____

Answers to "The Story of Aeneas"
Comprehension Questions and Vocabulary Exercises

Discussion Questions

1. Why did Aeneas leave Troy?

It had been destroyed by the Greeks. He had to leave or he, too, would have been destroyed.

2. Describe the Harpies and their anger towards Aeneas and his followers.

The Harpies were monsters who had the wings, talons and bodies of birds of prey but faces of women. They were angry because the Trojans slaughtered some of their cattle for food.

3. What was Jupiter's prediction for Aeneas?

Jupiter had predicted that Aeneas would build a city in Italy. He also predicted that his son would become king and his ancestors would found Rome.

4. Why did Dido kill herself?

The gods told Aeneas to leave Carthage and he obeyed. Dido was so in love with Aeneas that she could not bear to live without him.

5. How did the Harpies' prophecy come true?

The Trojans were eating their meal on flat cakes. When they finished, they were still hungry so they ate the flat cakes, too. The flat cakes were like their tables.

Look up each word in the dictionary and write its definition.

Vengeance: action in return for an injury or offense

Foul: disgusting in looks, taste, or smell

Despondent: feeling quite discouraged or depressed

Meager: thin, sparse; not enough

Soothsayer: a person who claims to foretell events

Fill in the blank with the correct vocabulary word.

1. The <u>meager</u> meal was not enough for one person, let alone four.

2. The predictions of the <u>soothsayer</u> seemed to come true.

3. The <u>foul</u> odor was bad enough to make everyone leave the party.

4. The king wanted to get even; his <u>vengeance</u> put fear in everyone.

5. She was <u>despondent</u> after he left because she missed him so much.

Match the vocabulary word to its antonym.

_B_	1. Vengeance	A.	Plentiful
_D_	2. Foul	B.	Truce
_E_	3. Despondent	C.	Historian
_A_	4. Meager	D.	Pleasant
_C_	5. Soothsayer	E.	Happy

The Story of Aeneas
Creative-Thinking Questions

1. Why do you think Juno wanted to destroy Aeneas?

_____

_____

_____

_____

2. What might have happened had Venus not helped Aeneas and his followers?

_____

_____

_____

_____

3. How might the Trojans have kept the Harpies from getting so angry, yet satisfied their hunger?

_____

_____

_____

_____

4. Why, do you think, did Neptune help the Trojans?

_____

_____

_____

_____

5. What part did Cupid play in the story of Aeneas? Did Cupid affect his future? Explain.

_____

_____

_____

_____

6. Predict what his life would have been like if Aeneas had stayed with Dido.

_____

_____

_____

_____

7. Was it right for Aeneas to take Lavinia from Turnus? Why or why not?

_____

_____

_____

_____

8. How did Aeneas and Lavinia's relationship affect the story?

_____

_____

_____

_____

9. What kind of leader do you think Ascanius became?

_____

_____

_____

_____

The Story of Aeneas
NOT AGAIN!

Create another challenge that Aeneas and his followers had to overcome.
Write about it.

The Story of Aeneas
PLEASE HELP US

What would you have to do to persuade Juno to side with the Trojans?
Write about it.

The Story of Aeneas
CREATE A POEM

Write a poem that would celebrate Aeneas becoming a god.

The Story of Aeneas
IN HIS HONOR

Create a statue of Aeneas that would celebrate his greatness for rescuing the Trojans and for founding a new city.

Gods and Goddess of Ancient Rome

Jupiter: Master of the gods and main god of the Romans. He held a thunderbolt in his hand. He is god of the sky. It is believed by the Romans that he brought light each day. His symbols are the thunderbolt and eagle. (Greek equivalent: Zeus)

Juno: Wife of Jupiter. She is the goddess of women and fertility. She is also the goddess of the heavens and heavenly light, especially moonlight. Her symbols are the pomegranate and a peacock. She is portrayed as a mother holding a flower in one hand and a baby in the other. (Greek equivalent: Hera)

Mars: God of war. He is also the god of spring, growth in nature, fertility and the protector of cattle. He is the strongest and most fearsome god except for Jupiter. He is portrayed as a warrior in full battle armor, wearing a crested helmet and carrying a shield. (Greek equivalent: Ares)

Venus: Goddess of love and beauty. She was also known as the goddess of the home. (Greek equivalent: Aphrodite)

Minerva: Goddess of wisdom, learning, art crafts and industry. Her symbol was the owl. (Greek equivalent: Athene)

Neptune: Brother to Jupiter. He is the god of the sea. His symbol is the trident. (Greek equivalent: Poseidon)

Pluto: Originally was god of wealth because of the gold, silver, and other valuable materials found beneath the earth. Because these things were mined, he later became recognized as the god of the physical underworld and later still as the god of the spiritual underworld. At that time (when he came to be associated with Hades) he was also considered brother to Jupiter and Neptune. (Greek equivalent: Hades)

Diana: Goddess of the hunting and the moon.(Greek equivalent: Artemis)

Mercury: Messenger of the gods. He traveled very quickly using his winged helmet. and sandals. He was the god of travelers and tradesmen. (Greek equivalent: Hermes)

Ceres: Goddess of the harvest. She is depicted carrying a bundle of grain. (Greek equivalent: Demeter)

Vesta: Goddess of the hearth and home. She was important to Rome because her temple held a flame that could not go out or bad luck would come to the empire. (Greek equivalent: Hestia)

Vulcan: The god of fire. He was also known as the blacksmith god and the volcano god. (Greek equivalent: Hephaestus)

Research Unit Directions

Choose a god or goddess to research.

SOURCES

Choose three resources to use for your research. One of them may be an internet source.

BLOOM QUESTIONS

Read about Bloom's Taxonomy on pages 118–119. Using the template, write a Bloom question from each level based upon the mythology regarding your god or goddess to help you with your research. When you have completed the Bloom questions, you will begin your research.

NOTE CARDS

Not all the information in your resources will be important for your research. You will break the information down into categories, or topics, and record the important information onto note cards. This is a good way to get organized when working on a research topic.

Use a different color note card for each source. (If you don't have colored cards, you may use a sticker or a colored dot. The first card of each color should contain the bibliographic information. Each card within the color set will pertain to a particular category. Write a different category at the top of each card. (See pages 120–121.) As you do your research, you will put the information on your note cards.

BIBLIOGRAPHY

Create a bibliography of the sources you have used. (See page 122 for the proper format.)

OUTLINE

After completing your research using your three sources, use your note cards to organize the information into an outline. Each category on the note cards will become the Roman numerals for your outline. (See page 123 for an example of the outline.)

PRODUCT

After you complete your outline, you are ready to choose a product that will reflect your research. (See page 124 for product ideas.) Fill out a product proposal using the form on page 128. This will help you plan your product. When the product is finished, evaluate it by using the product evaluation form on page 125.

PRESENTATION

You are now ready to give their presentations. See pages 126–127 for presentation tips. Page 129 includes a scoring rubric that can be used to score the completed research project.

Levels of Bloom's Taxonomy

Benjamin Bloom divided educational questions into six main categories: knowledge, comprehension, application, analysis, synthesis and evaluation. The last four levels promote critical and creative thinking.

Level	Skill Involved
Knowledge:	simple recall
Comprehension:	understanding of the material
Application:	applying learned information to a new situation
Analysis:	the breaking down of learned knowledge into small parts
Synthesis:	creating something new and original from the acquired knowledge
Evaluation:	making a judgment and backing it up

The following verbs can help in writing Bloom questions.

Knowledge: list, know, define, relate, repeat, recall, specify, tell, name

Comprehension: recognize, restate, explain, describe, summarize, express, review, discuss, identify, locate, report, retell

Application: demonstrate, interview, simulate, dramatize, experiment, show, use, employ, operate, exhibit, apply, calculate, solve, illustrate

Analysis: compare, examine, categorize, group, test, inventory, probe, analyze, discover, arrange, organize, contrast, classify, survey

Synthesis: plan, develop, invent, predict, propose, produce, arrange, formulate, construct, incorporate, originate, create, prepare, design, set up

Evaluation: value, recommend, evaluate, criticize, estimate, decide, conclude, predict, judge, compare, rate, measure, select, infer

Bloom Questions

Knowledge
1. List the parts of _____.
2. Define how to _____.
3. What does _____ mean?

Comprehension
1. Describe how to _____.
2. Explain how _____ happened.
3. Locate where _____ is found.

Application
1. Demonstrate how to _____.
2. Tell how to operate a _____.
3. Dramatize how _____ is different today.

Analysis
1. Compare and contrast _____ and _____.
2. How would you test _____?
3. Organize _____ and test it.

Synthesis
1. Plan a new way to _____.
2. Create a new _____. Explain it.
3. Design a way to _____.

Evaluation
1. Judge the usefulness of _____.
2. Predict how _____ may change _____.
3. Recommend _____ to someone.

Note Cards and Organization

Use color-coded note cards. Put all the information from one source on cards of the same color. For example, all pink cards may refer to a certain book; all blue cards may come from an internet source; all white cards come from a magazine source; etc.

Make sure the first card of a color has the resource information. (See card No. 1.) **You can find this information on the title page and the reverse side of the title page.** Each note card should have a title or category describing what that card is about. (See Card No. 2.)

Card No. 1

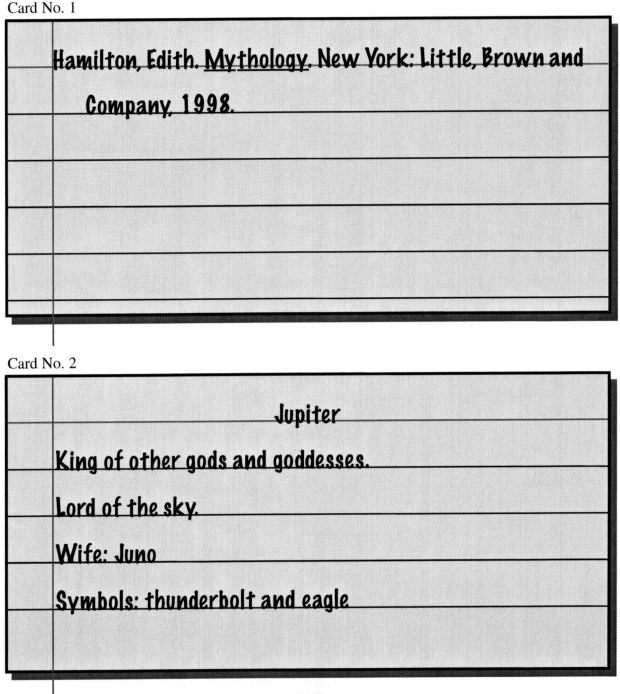

Hamilton, Edith. <u>Mythology.</u> New York: Little, Brown and
Company, 1998.

Card No. 2

Jupiter

King of other gods and goddesses.

Lord of the sky.

Wife: Juno

Symbols: thunderbolt and eagle

Bibliographies

A **bibliography** is a list of books and other sources of information. There are two main reasons to have a bibliography. First of all, it shows the research an author has done in preparing the work. It also tells readers where they can look if they want more information on the subject.

Each entry includes important information:

- Title of the Book
- Author's Name
- Name of Publisher
- Copyright Date

Entries are listed in alphabetical order. Alphabetical order is based on the first important word in the entry. Usually, that will be the author's last name. If an entry begins with a title, do not use the words "A," "An," or "The" to put the entries in order.

Bibliographies should be easy to read. Put a line space between each entry. Also, indent all lines in an entry except the first.

General Rules

Begin each entry at the left margin.

Indent all lines of an entry except the first.

Authors' names are written last name first.

If there are more than one author, write them in the same order as on the title page.

Alphabetize by the first important word in the entry. (Do not use "A," "An," or "The.")

Book and magazine titles should be printed in italics or underlined.

Tiles of articles in magazines are put in quotation marks.

Each entry should end with a period.

Skip a line between each entry.

Bibliography Formats

Follow the appropriate format for each type of resource. Be sure to notice the punctuation as well as the order of the information.

NOTE: If typed or handwritten, titles may be underlined instead of being done in italics. When no author is given, start with the name of the article.

Book Written by One Author:

Author's Last Name, Author's First Name. *Title of Book.* City Where Published: Publisher, Copyright Date.

Book Written by More Than One Author:

1st Author's Last Name, 1st Author's First Name, and 2nd Author's First and Last Name. (The rest is the same.)

If the same author has written more than one of the books, you may use a dash instead of the name. Alphabetize by the book title.

Encyclopedias and Other Reference Books:

Author's Last Name, Author's First Name (If known). "Title of Article." *Title of Reference Book.* Year of the Edition Used.

If you use an on-line encyclopedia, add the date you visited the site.

Magazines:

Author's Last Name, Author's First Name (If known). "Title of Article." *Magazine Name.* Date on Magazine: page(s).

World Wide Web:

Author's Last Name, Author's First Name (If known). "Title of Article." *Title of Work* (if there is one). Date you visited the site. <complete http address>.

Personal Interview:

Last Name, First Name. Personal Interview. Date Interviewed.

Outline Example
The Beginning of Roman Mythology

I. Reasons for Mythology
   A. Explain natural occurrences
   B. Desire for organized religion

II. Most myths taken from Greek mythology.

III. Main Gods
   A. Jupiter
      1. ruler of other gods and goddesses
      2. lord of the sky
      3. symbols
         a. thunderbolt
         b. eagle
   B. Juno
      1. wife of Jupiter and queen of gods and goddesses
      2. goddess of beginnings of the months
      3. goddess of birth
      4. symbols are a mother with flower and baby
   C..Cupid: god of love
   D. Mars
      1. God of War
      2. Symbols
         a. wolf
         b. woodpecker
         c. lance
   D. Venus: goddess of love
   E. Vulcan: God of Fire
   F. Neptune: God of Sea

IV. Ceremonies
   A. Family rituals
      1. To ensure success in life and work
      2. Shrine
      3. Gifts
         a. incense
         b. food and wine
   B. Compitalia
      1. To bring life and health to land
      2. Plough, wooden doll for free household members
      3. Wooden ball for slaves
         a. incense
         b. food and wine
   C. Saturnalia
      1. Feast to honor Saturn for good harvest
      2. Slaves and masters change places for festival
   D. Matronalia
      1. Feast to honor Juno celebrated first day of March
      2. Husbands give wives gifts

Product Ideas

diary

collection

puzzle

scrapbook

cartoon

invention

play

report

model

game

photograph display

teach a lesson

want ad

TV commercial

new theory

overhead transparency

display

story

brochure

mural

greeting card

diagram

speech

book cover

audio tape

advertisement

poem

radio show

graph

map

diorama

magazine article

pop-up book

sculpture

new product

skit

flip book

secret code

newspaper article

puppet show

time line

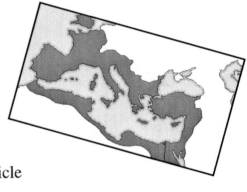

Product Self-Evaluation

Are you pleased with your product? Why or why not?

_____

_____

_____

Do you think your product reflects your research? How?

_____

_____

_____

_____

If you scored your product, 1 being the lowest and 10 being the highest, what score would you give it? Circle one.

1   2   3   4   5   6   7   8   9   10

Give some reasons why you scored your product as you did.

_____

_____

_____

Did you enjoy making your product? Why or why not?

_____

_____

_____

Presentation Guidelines

Organize your presentation using the following outline. No matter what product you choose, you will have to present your information orally to the class. Use notes to help you present your research and your product.

I. Introduction
    A. Include a topic sentence.
    B. Be sure to grab your audience's attention.

II. Body
    A. This will be the major part of your presentation of your product.
    B. Include important information.
    C. Know your information so that you refer to your notes as little as possible.
    D. Show any visuals you have included.

III. Conclusion
    A. Summarize your presentation with one or two sentences.
    B. Do not include any new material.
    C. Ask for questions.

The topic or introductory sentence should "grab" your audiences' attention.

The body is your product presented.
o   Do not read from your product.
o   Know the information.
o   Tell the class about what you learned.
o   Show your product.

1. Know your topic and material well.
2. Be organized. Have your materials and information ready to use in your presentation.
3. Practice your presentation:
    • Do not read your presentation.
    • Give your presentation to anyone who will listen. Practice with your parents, your siblings, even your pets. The more often you give the presentation, the better and more comfortable you will become.
4. Make good eye contact with your audience.
5. Stand up straight, move a little, and don't stand in a frozen stance.
6. Use an oral presentation format:
    • Introduce your topic.
    • Explain each point you are trying to make.
    • Summarize your presentation with one or two sentences.
    • Ask if there are any questions.
7. Never turn your back on the audience.
8. Make sure your audience can hear you clearly.

Oral Presentation Tips

1. Know your topic and material well.

2. Be organized. Have your materials and information ready to use in your presentation.

3. Practice your presentation:

   • Do not read your presentation.

   • Give your presentation to anyone who will listen. Practice with your parents, your siblings, even your pets. The more often you give the presentation, the better and more comfortable you will become.

4. Make good eye contact with your audience.

5. Stand up straight, move a little, and don't stand in a frozen stance.

6. Use an oral presentation format:

   • Introduce your topic.

   • Explain each point you are trying to make.

   • Summarize your presentation with one or two sentences.

   • Ask if there are any questions.

7. Never turn your back on the audience.

8. Make sure your audience can hear you clearly.

   • Speak slowly so everyone can understand you.

Product Proposal

Name of Product: _____

Supplies needed to make the product:

_____   _____

_____   _____

_____   _____

_____   _____

_____   _____

Steps needed to make the product:

1._____

2._____

3._____

4._____

5._____

6._____

Did you have any problems?

_____

_____

_____

What could you do differently to make the product better?

_____

_____

_____

Research Project Grading

Name: _____

Resources: _____ (1-10 points)
___ Do you have three resources?
___ Is no more than one resource from the internet?

Note Cards: _____ (1-20 points)
___ Is the correct format used?
___ Is there no plagiarism?
___ Are the sources cited on the note cards?

Outline: _____ (1-10 points)
___ How well is the outline organized?
___ Does the outline reflect the research?

Research Presentation: _____ (1-30 points)
___ Was the audience attentive?
___ Did the presentation flow nicely?
___ Did the quality of ideas reflect higher-level thinking?
___ Did the conclusion summarize the research?

Bibliography: _____ (1-10 points)
___ Was the correct format used?
___ Were all the sources included?

Product: _____ (1-20 points)
___ Does the product reflect the research?
___ Is the product challenging?
___ Does the overall quality of product reflect hard work and careful research?

Bibliography

BOOKS

Bullfinch, Thomas. *A Book of Myths*. New York: Macmillan Publishing Company, 1980.

Carlile, Vowery. *Ready to Research Ancient Civilizations*. Hawthorne, NJ: Educational Impressions, Inc., 2006.

Hamilton, Edith. *Mythology*. New York: Little Brown and Company, 1998.

McAlpine, Jim and Marion Finkbinder, Sue Jeweler and Betty Weincek. *As It Was! Ancient Rome*. Hawthorne, NJ: Educational Impressions, Inc., 2001.

Stark, Rebecca. *Mythology*. Hawthorne, NJ: Educational Impressions, Inc., 2001.

Usher, Kerry. *Heroes, Gods & Emperors from Roman Mythology*. New York: Peter Bedrick Books, 1983.

WORLD WIDE WEB

" Minotaur." 2006. http://www.waltm.net/minotaur.htm